Warro

goes on an adventure

*Join me on my adventure and
when you see this paint pot
add as many more types of information
to the pictures as you can.
Why not add some colour throughout
the book as well?*

This book belongs to

....

Our special friend Warro, the kind data bear,
Loves to explore and never minds where.
On her latest adventure, such strange things she found,
Let's share them with you, as they're sure to astound.

As she wandered along, enjoying the weather,
In front of her suddenly floated a feather.
She smiled as it fluttered along an old path,
Each time it escaped her, making her laugh.

The feather flew on, our Warro gave chase,
She followed it further, to a new and strange place.
Then came to a door, nestled into a mound,
And the feather gently landed, right there on the ground.

Warro carefully opened the creaky old door,
The warped, scarred timbers scraped the dirt floor.
A pale dusty light lit up her kind features,
And she smiled as she spied all the paper made creatures.

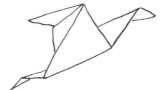

Wafting towards her as the door stood agape,
Came critters torn from pages, paper birds of all shapes.
Warro took a step into this strange paper land,
No going back now as the door loudly slammed.

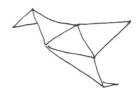

In front of her now rolling hills made of ledgers,
All covered with lines of hand-written treasures.
Right there on the pages were dates and some names,
Notes scrawled on edges, random thoughts, idle claims.

Past a pale parchment hill, to a bright babbling brook,
Warro peered into the water, to get a close look.
A riverbed made up of notes and reports,
From doctors and schools, even records of sports.

On the banks of the river lay details of work,
If people tried hard or had tended to shirk.
Warro stared as the water flowed on underground,
Wading in, feeling sure there was more to be found.

She clambered through weeds that were all points of view,
All these things written down, so much data on you.
Warro jumped in and swam to a cave filled with lights,
All around was more data and further insights.

The things in this cave she found so surreal,
A digital world with no touch and no feel.
In this place built by screens without eyes or a face,
Were thoughts and ideas all made in cyberspace.

Warro found in this world she could change her outfit,
This was really quite fun she had to admit.
This new cyber world where millions can play,
We can all of us choose what we want to display.

"I may be a bear," said Warro with glee,
"But in this world, no-one need know it is me.
I can change to a zebra with wings or a mouse,
And even pretend that my home's a lighthouse."

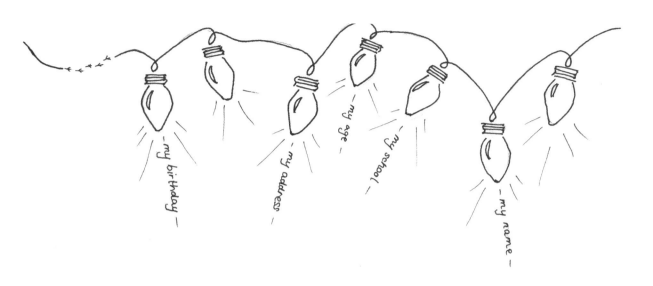

She ventured on further and the lights told a tale,
All the trails left online, all her clicks and details,
Collected from all the web games and the chats,
All the places she'd been could be found in these stats.

But these details combined can tell so much more,
Your messages and emails, all the secrets it stores.
It knows just who you are and the people you like,
It knows when you've searched online for that bike.

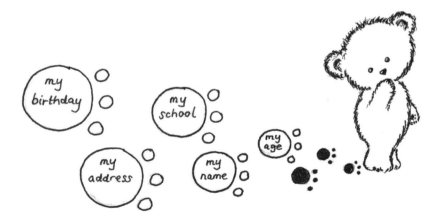

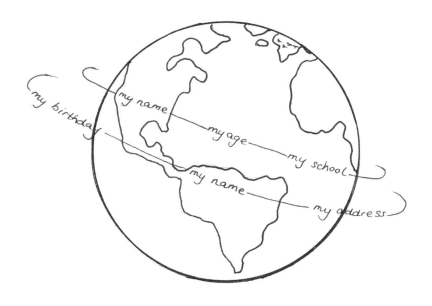

All this data around, it just didn't stop,
Thank goodness there's nobody here to eavesdrop.
But wait, all that data they're trying to probe,
Just look, it's all being sent round the globe.

Warro wondered and gawped feeling stunned by the sight,
She could see private chats and that didn't feel right.
They were all being processed, traded and stored,
Feeding vast greedy engines wanting data to hoard.

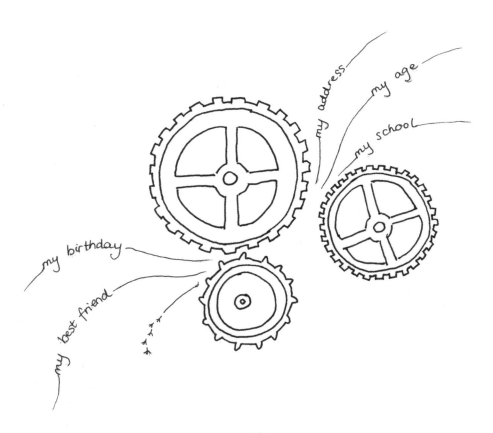

Treading carefully on, unsure of her footing,
Realising now that strangers could be looking.
Then a feather appeared, just like before,
It fluttered and settled right there on the floor.

Warro saw in the dirt, some words could be seen,
She bent down to read, wondering what it could mean.
"Dear Warro a few simple rules here are key,
They're important protection for you and for me."

The words on the ground carried on to advise,
"Just think before sharing your data, be wise.
Pause before giving your home and your name,
Some people out there really aren't what they claim."

Think

Warro realised this world needed treating with care,
Even if just for now she's a digital bear.
Whether chatting or playing a new online game,
Be safe and not sorry – please don't feel any shame.

Warro searched all around for a corner of peace,
Scared this commotion would just never cease.
At last, a quiet spot, she sat down for a rest,
Wishing for an end to this peculiar quest.

And then, in a corner, Warro noticed some stairs,
Knowing by then this was no place for bears.
Climbing up to a door in the dim growing light,
On up through some tree roots, she left the false night.

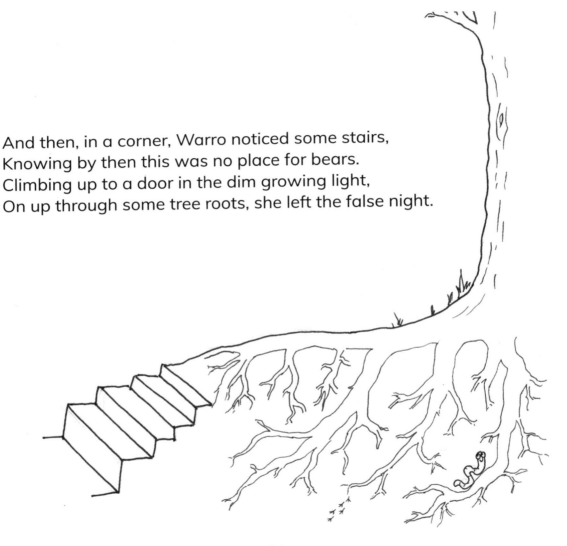

Emerging beneath a large beautiful tree,
"At last, something real," Warro cried out with glee.
"A world full of grass, of leaves and of petals,
I'm finally out of that world made of metal."

As she sat underneath the lovely old tree,
Warro heard a strange fluttering, what could it be?
Then out of the branches a small bird flew down,
With blue on his head like a sweet feathered crown.

Bijou the Bluetit had been there all along,
Watching to make sure that nothing would go wrong.
"Dear Bijou – please do come and sit on my arm,
It was you all that time helping keep me from harm."

Together the friends talked of the places they'd been,
Of what they had learned and what they had seen.
Of how both the learning and fun needn't be missed,
Just think before sharing and consider this list ...

Who is asking?

What do they want to know?

Why do they want it?

Where will it go?

Who is asking

Why do they want it

What do they want to know

Where will it go

31

My name means "Hi" in Guernsey's local language.

It begins with the letter W,
just like the words
I want you to remember
when sharing your data.

Who – Why – What – Where?